Blippi™

A Very Merry Blippi Christmas!

studio fun
INTERNATIONAL

Hooray, Christmas is coming.
It's my favorite time of the year!

How do we look?

I love when it snows at Christmastime!

It's fun to build a snowman. Can you build one here?

Fa, la, la, la, la!
The holidays make me want to sing!

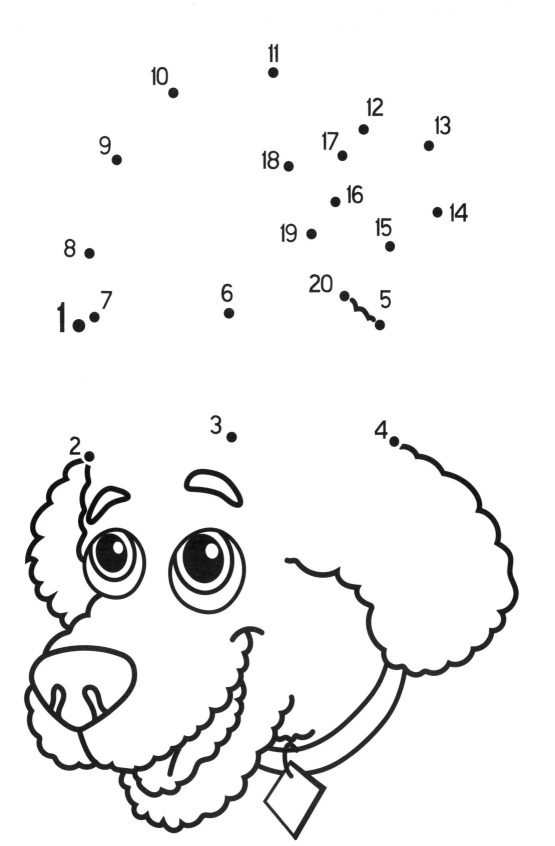

Connect the dots to help Lyno get ready for Christmas!

Let's pick out a Christmas tree!

8

I can't wait to get the tree home so I can decorate it!

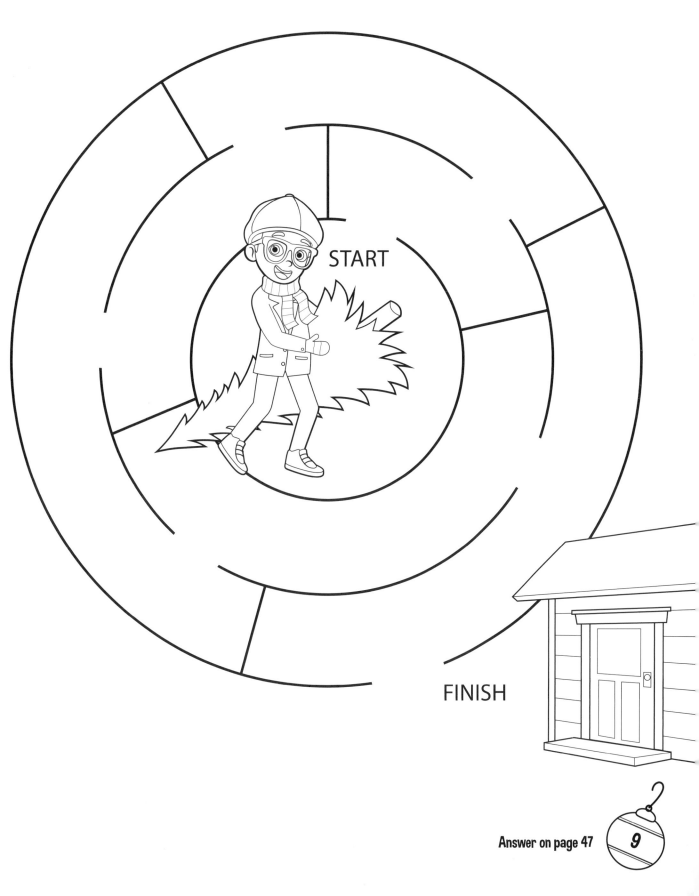

START

FINISH

Answer on page 47

9

Now it's starting to look like Christmas!

Can you decorate this Christmas tree for me?

Can you spot three differences in the town's decorations from the picture below and the one on the next page?

Draw something you think Lyno might like for Christmas.

14

Whee! Look at us!

15

Santa will be here soon.

How many stars can you count in the night sky?

Answer on page 47

Christmas is such a sweet time!

Cookies and milk are ready for Santa!

19

**Draw some cookies
you think Santa will enjoy.**

20

Yum, these are special gingerbread cookies!

Find and circle the two that are exactly the same, and then color them all.

Find and circle the present that is not like the others. Then color them all.

22

Answer on page 47

It's shaping up to be a great Christmas. Find and put a check mark next to each shape you find in the picture below. Use the clue box to help you!

- ☐ square
- ☐ rectangle
- ☐ circle
- ☐ triangle
- ☐ star
- ☐ diamond
- ☐ heart
- ☐ crescent

Snow much fun!
Find the snowflake that is
different in each row.

Answers on page 48

Whoa, it's a challenge to balance, but we can do it!

Go fetch, Lyno!

This excavator needs Christmas decorations!
Can you draw some?

27

Find and circle the group with the most Christmas cards.

Choo choo!
Let's take a ride on the town's holiday train.

Draw a Santa hat for Lyno.

Smile!

31

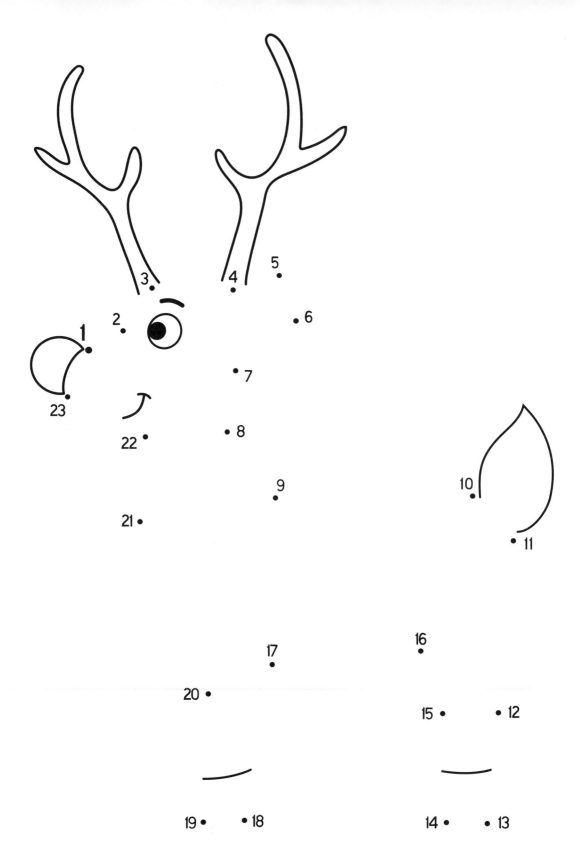

Connect the dots to see one of Santa's important Christmas Eve helpers.

Answer on page 48

Christmas begins with the letter C.
Circle these Christmas things
that also begin with a C.

Answer on page 48

We're ready if Santa needs
help with deliveries!

34

Help me put the presents under the tree!

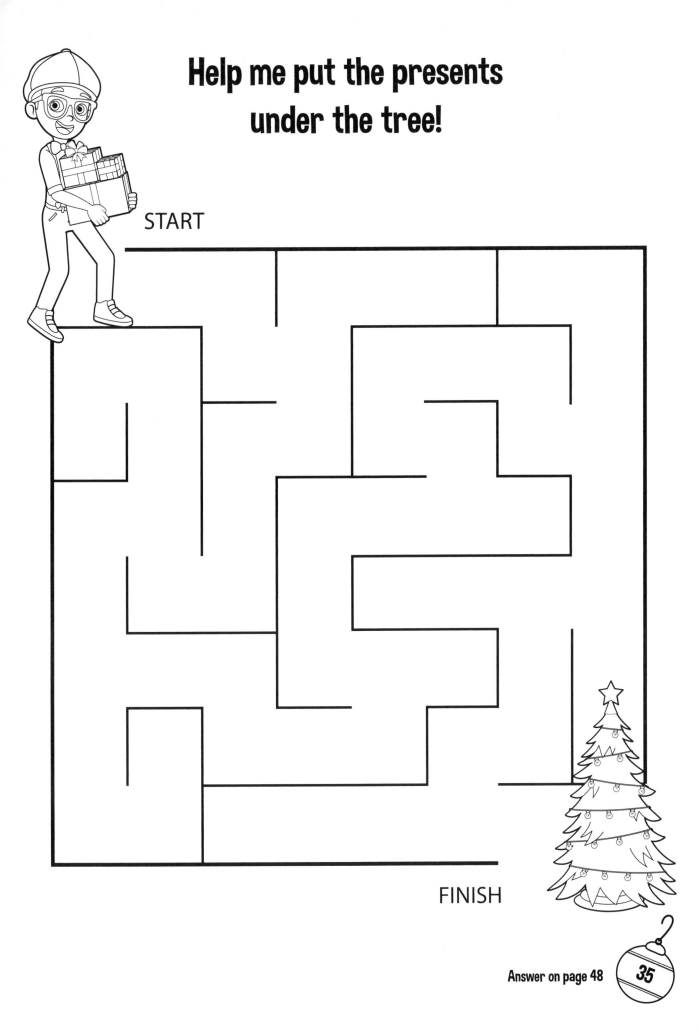

START

FINISH

Answer on page 48

Wow, we're at the North Pole!

We're looking for Santa's workshop.
Can you draw it for us?

Follow the letters of my name to get me to the Christmas tree.

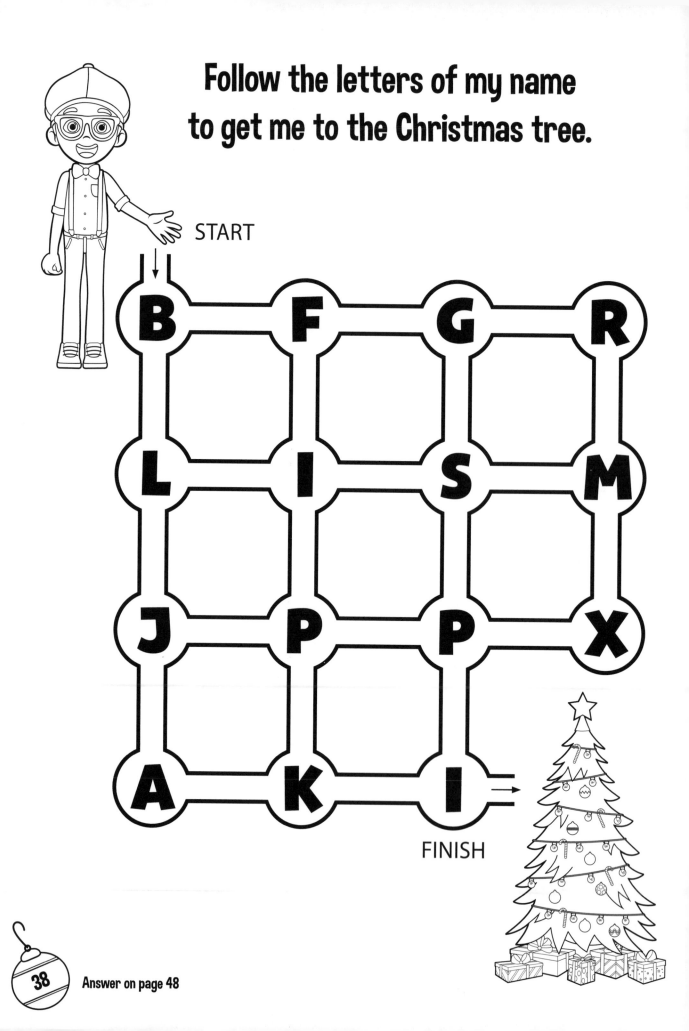

START

B F G R

L I S M

J P P X

A K I

FINISH

"'Twas the Night Before Christmas..."

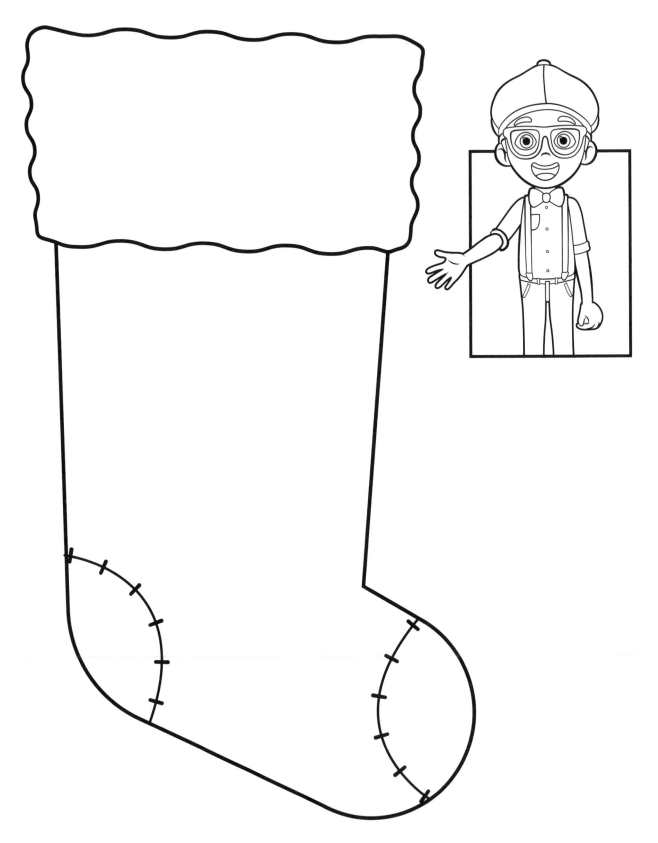

I need to hang up my Christmas stocking.
Can you decorate it so Santa knows it's mine?

40

Can you decorate Lyno's Christmas stocking?

41

I love Christmas colors but my favorite colors are still orange and blue!

1. Green

2. Red

3. Orange

4. Blue

Use the color key to color in the gifts.

43

Circle the group with the most Christmas bells.

Answer on page 48

Christmas is a time to share with others.

My favorite present is YOU!
Merry Christmas!

Answers

page 7

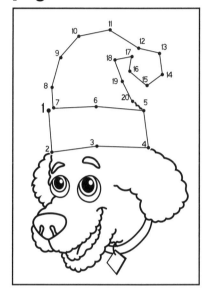

page 9

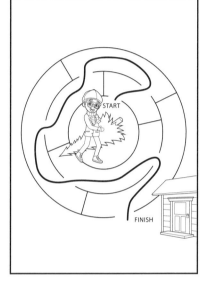

page 13

pages 16-17

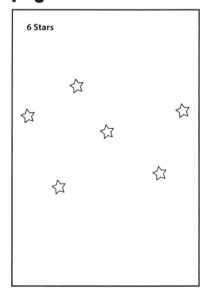

6 Stars

page 21

page 22

Answers

page 23

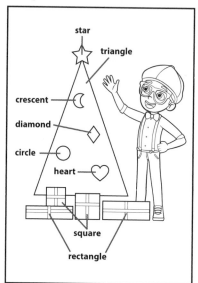

star

triangle

crescent

diamond

circle

heart

square

rectangle

page 24

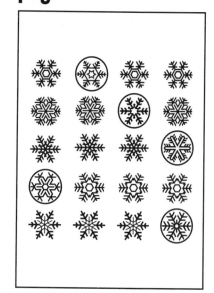

page 28

page 32

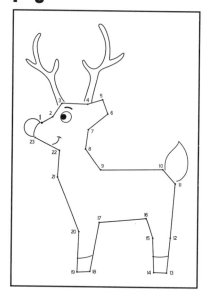

page 33

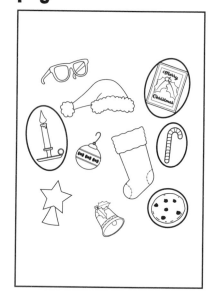

page 35

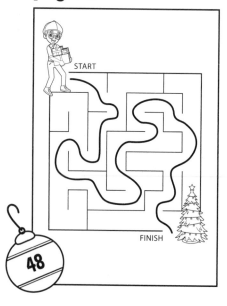

START

FINISH

48

page 38

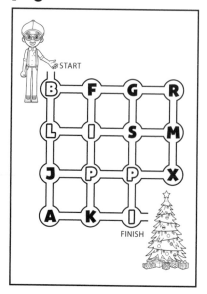

START

B	F	G	R
L	I	S	M
J	P	P	X
A	K	I	

FINISH

page 44

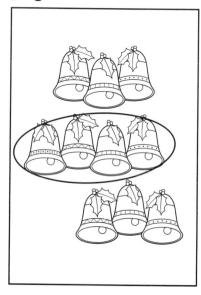